MARVEL HEROES

MOVIE THEATER STORYBOOK
Adapted by Michael Teitelbaum

CONTENTS

Reader's
Digest
Children's Books®

New York , New York • Montréal, Québec • Bath, United Kingdom

SPIDER-MAN

Peter Parker was one of the best and brightest students at Midtown High School. Science was his favorite subject. Peter lived with his Aunt May and Uncle Ben. One night, Peter went to a special exhibit at a science lab. "This should be fun!" he said.

At the lab, a scientist talked about an experiment using a radioactive spider. Little did Peter know, as he watched and listened, that the tiny radioactive spider in that lab would change his life forever!

DISK 1

1

2 "Oww!" Peter cried out in pain, as the radioactive spider bit him on the hand! "I feel sick," Peter said. He rushed home and went right to bed.

The next morning, however, Peter discovered that he could do all kinds of amazing things. He could leap 30 feet into the air. He could stick to walls and crawl up the side of a building. He could even crush a metal pipe with his bare hand!

3

"That spider bite must have given me these spider-like powers," Peter said.

4 ▶ He scampered along thin telephone wires, then scrambled down a brick wall. There, he spotted a sign offering $100 to anyone who could beat Crusher Hogan, the wrestler.

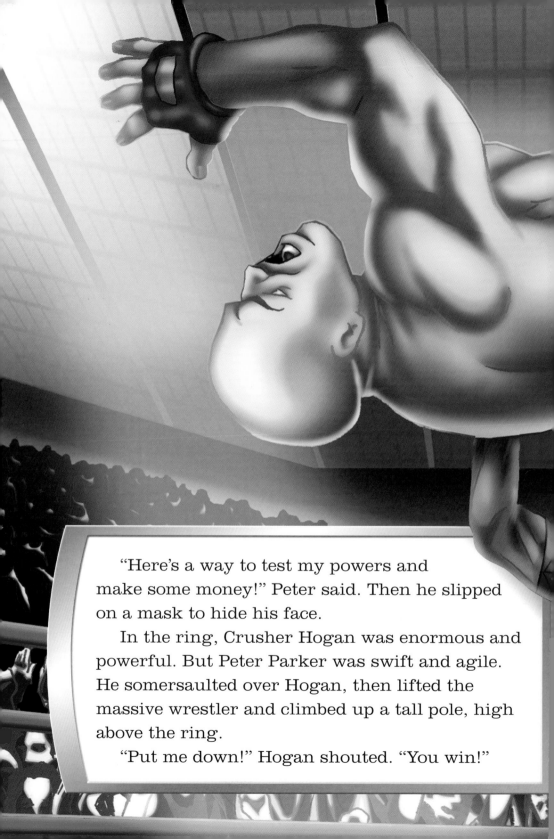

"Here's a way to test my powers and make some money!" Peter said. Then he slipped on a mask to hide his face.

In the ring, Crusher Hogan was enormous and powerful. But Peter Parker was swift and agile. He somersaulted over Hogan, then lifted the massive wrestler and climbed up a tall pole, high above the ring.

"Put me down!" Hogan shouted. "You win!"

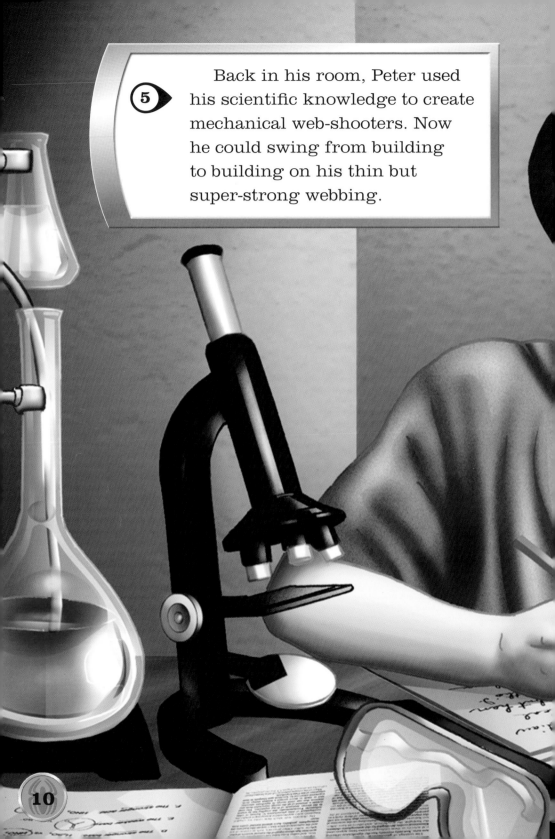

Back in his room, Peter used his scientific knowledge to create mechanical web-shooters. Now he could swing from building to building on his thin but super-strong webbing.

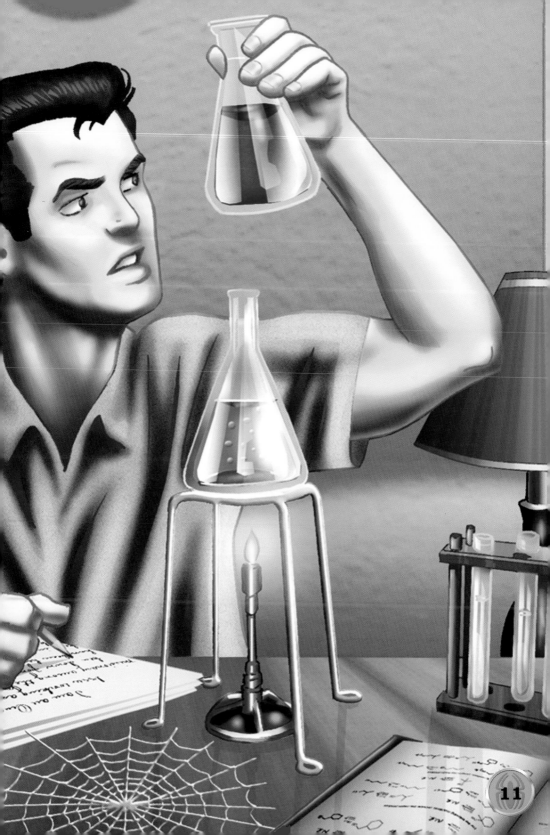

"I need to hide my identity," Peter said. "And I need a cool costume!"

So Peter created a costume and a mask with a spider-web pattern.

"I have spider powers and a spider costume," Peter said. "From now on, I'll call myself...SPIDER-MAN!"

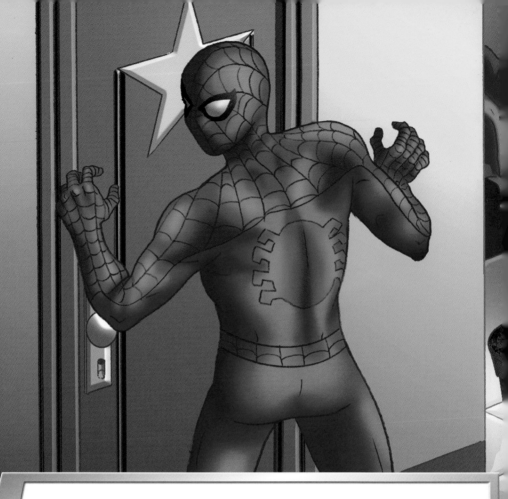

Spider-Man showed off his amazing powers on a TV show. Backstage, after the show, a man raced past him. "Stop that man!" shouted a police officer. "He's a thief!"

But Spider-Man stood by as the thief slipped into an elevator and got away.

"Why didn't you do something?" the officer asked. "With your powers, you could have easily stopped that guy!"

"Why should I do your job for free?" Spider-Man replied. "I get paid to use my powers."

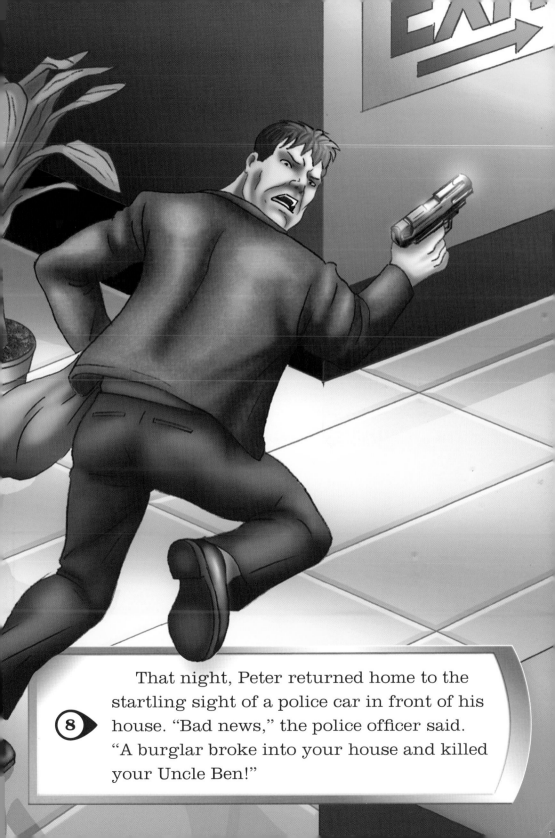

That night, Peter returned home to the startling sight of a police car in front of his house. "Bad news," the police officer said. "A burglar broke into your house and killed your Uncle Ben!"

8

9 Peter was stunned. He quickly slipped into his Spider-Man costume and set out to capture the thief who had murdered his beloved uncle. But when Spider-Man caught the thief, he was shocked to discover that he was the same man who **10** had run past him at the television studio.

"I should have stopped him when I had the chance!" Spider-Man cried.

And so, Spider-Man learned that with great power must also come great responsibility.

Spider-Man decided to use his powers to fight crime. Over the years, he battled many Super Villains.

11 Spider-Man discovered that when danger was near, his body tingled with a strange energy. One day his spider-sense gave him a jolt.

"Danger must be near," said the Web-Slinger, as he swung from building to building.

Spider-Man was right! One very dangerous foe Spider-Man faced was Doctor Octopus. This evil scientist had four powerful mechanical arms that he controlled with his mind. He used his arms for all kinds of evil purposes, including a string of robberies meant to finance his sinister plots.

Battling Spider-Man, Doc Ock grabbed
the Web-Slinger with his massive metal arms.
"He's too strong!" Spider-Man groaned,
trying to free himself. "Can't break loose!"
Suddenly, Spider-Man fired a glob of sticky

13 webbing right into Doc Ock's eyes. The Super
Villain released the Wall-Crawler, who swung
to safety. Doc Ock escaped, but would go on
to plague Spider-Man for years to come.

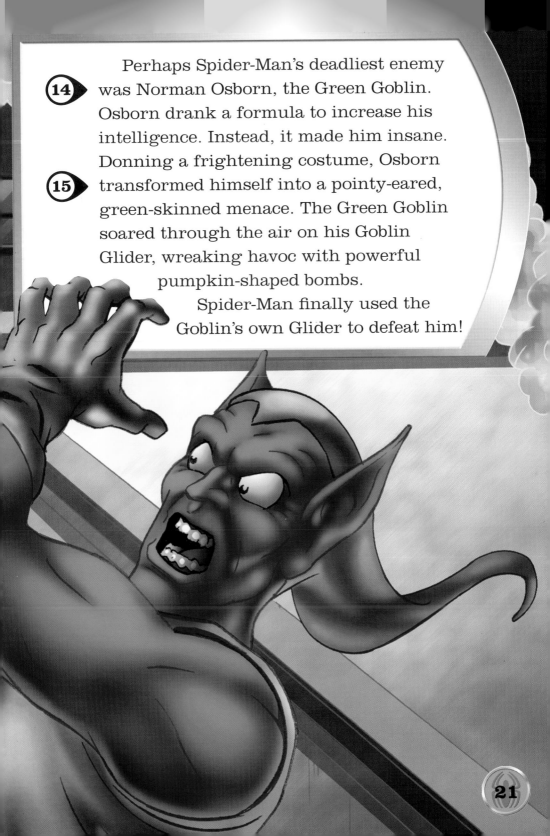

Perhaps Spider-Man's deadliest enemy **14** ▶ was Norman Osborn, the Green Goblin. Osborn drank a formula to increase his intelligence. Instead, it made him insane. Donning a frightening costume, Osborn **15** ▶ transformed himself into a pointy-eared, green-skinned menace. The Green Goblin soared through the air on his Goblin Glider, wreaking havoc with powerful pumpkin-shaped bombs.

Spider-Man finally used the Goblin's own Glider to defeat him!

Then Spider-Man swung off into the night, ever ready to battle the forces of evil.